My Dress-up Ballerinas Sticker Book

How to use this book:

The ballerinas in this book need some help deciding what to wear. Find the right stickers for each page, then choose clothes and accessories for each girl. There are a lot of extra stickers to decorate the pages, and don't forget the activities on the back of your sticker sheets, too!

Parragon

Bath · New York · Singapore · Hong Kong · Cologne · Delhi · Melbourne

Hello, ballerinas!

Here are four ballerinas, all ready for a busy week at Ballet School. They don't like practicing much but they love to dance. One day, they're all going to be famous. Say hello, ballerinas!

Hi, I'm Abigail.

My name is Grace.

Ballet Lesson

Abigail and Grace have an early start at the ballet studio.
They wear leotards and skirts with matching silk slippers.
Their favorite colors are pink and lilac.
Can you find an outfit for each girl?

Roller-Skating

Megan and Emily take a break and go roller-skating in the park. They each wear a T-shirt with shorts or jogging pants, and carry a drink in case they get thirsty. Don't forget their roller skates!

An Audition

Abigail and Grace have auditions at the Dance School. They wear leotards with matching shoes and white leggings. For good luck, Abigail wears a locket, and Grace brings her favorite teddy bear.

Ballet Lesson stickers

Mirror Magic

Can you spot five differences between the two pictures below? Draw a circle around each difference in the bottom picture.

Different Dancer

Look at these pictures of ballerina Abigail.
Draw a circle around the one that's different.

Roller Skating stickers

Lovely Leotard

The ballerinas are looking for their favorite leotards.
Follow the lines to see who owns each leotard.

Amazing Maze

Which path should Abigail take through the
Ballet School garden to meet Megan?
Collect two tiaras on the way.

Aftershow Party stickers

udition stickers

Park Puzzle

One piece of the jigsaw puzzle is missing.
Draw a circle around the piece that fits.

Whose Shoes?

Draw a line to join each outfit with a pair
of matching shoes.

Ballet Math

Can you do this picture math?
Write your answers in the boxes.

Ballerina Beauties

Only two of the pictures below are exactly the same.
Draw a line to join the matching pictures.

Opening Night stickers

Dress Rehearsal stickers

Tutu Time

The ballerinas' tutus are mixed up. Follow the lines to find out which tutu belongs to each ballerina.

Dotty Dress

Join the dots to finish drawing the dress,
then color it in.

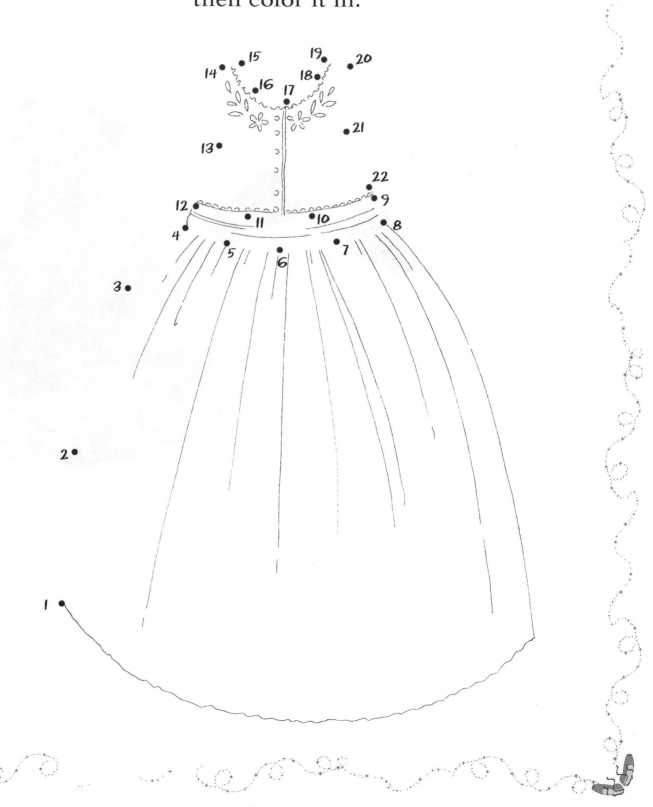

Dress Rehearsal sticker

Dress Rehearsal

Backstage in the dressing room, Emily and Megan are having loads of fun. They are trying on all kinds of costumes! Can you find each girl a beautiful dress with shoes and a shawl to match?

Opening Night

The ballerinas have just finished their first performance! Two girls wear sparkly leotards with full skirts, and the others wear frilly leotards with leggings. Find their matching shoes and crowns, too.

After-show Party

Everyone is invited to a HUGE party after the grand finale. The ballerinas wear a dress or jeans with a top, and their favorite party shoes for a night of dancing. They bring a little bag each, too.

Photo Album

The ballerinas have put some of their favorite snapshots into an album. Decorate the page with some of your extra stickers.

Abigail and Grace at the ballet studio.

A big round of applause for the ballerinas!

Emily and Megan get their skates on.

Smile, everyone!